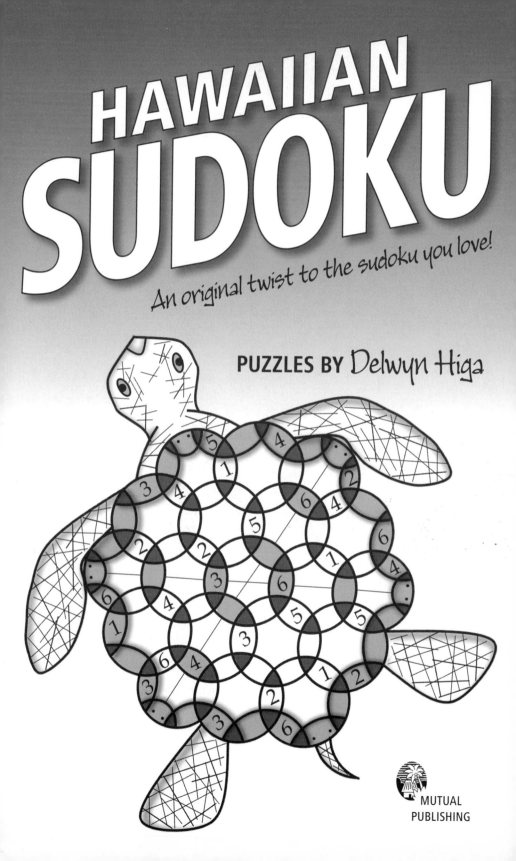

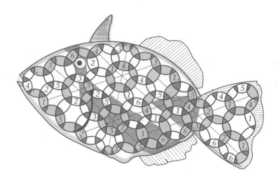

ISBN-10: 1-56647-948-7
ISBN-13: 978-1-56647-948-6

Third Printing, October 2013

Mutual Publishing, LLC
1215 Center Street, Suite 210
Honolulu, Hawai'i 96816
Ph: 808-732-1709 / Fax: 808-734-4094
email: info@mutualpublishing.com
www.mutualpublishing.com

Printed in Korea

Dedication

This book would not have been possible if it wasn't for a close and dear friend of mine named Jon Kubota. Several years back, I would go to Jon's house to visit him when he had ALS (Lou Gehrig's disease). To keep busy he enjoyed playing Sudoku. I didn't know what that was so I took a look at some of his puzzles.

Then I thought maybe I could create a different type of Sudoku for Jon to play, and I did. I had him try it, and he thought it was really good. He said, "Hey, you should make a book of this." So I tried to find a book publisher. It was a long and tough road, but I finally did it. Unfortunately, Jon isn't with us today to see this happen, but I owe it all to him for introducing Sudoku to me and for giving me the strength to persevere when I almost gave up. Thanks, Jon.

This one's for you.

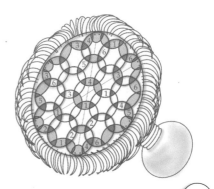

Acknowledgments

I would like to thank Jan Komatsu for her support, Eric Tang for testing and playing the puzzles whenever I needed his help, and Jane Gillespie (my production manager) for being so nice and helpful. A big mahalo to Mutual Publishing for giving me this opportunity.

Introduction

Aloha. I believe most of you have tried the puzzle Sudoku before. About 5 years ago this highly addictive puzzle swept around the world and became an instant phenomenon, and within a year it has become one of the most popular puzzles in history. Many Sudoku books have become best sellers and are still very popular today. The mass majority of Sudoku books are all the same: the puzzle has a square grid. Sudoku creators have been trying to make different variations with only little success. Sudoku addicts have been craving something new and exciting, and here it is: it's called Hawaiian Sudoku.

Delwyn Higa, the creator of Hawaiian Sudoku, designed this puzzle by taking the opposite approach. Technically, the opposite of a square is a "circle," and that's how he designed this puzzle. These puzzles were very creatively constructed in that the circles are formed into objects and animal patterns.

This is how it's played: the spaces around each and every circle it have to contain the numbers 1 through 6, with no repeated numbers. An added twist to this puzzle is that there are sections that go vertically, horizontally, or diagonally. These sections must contain the numbers 1 through 6 as well.

Delwyn was born and has lived in Hawai'i his whole life. He is a jewelry designer and a hand engraver of Hawaiian Heirloom Jewelry. As a matter of fact, many of the puzzle designs are based on forms he engraves on Hawaiian jewelry. His love for the Islands is what made him decide to give these puzzles a Hawaiian theme. There are 10 different patterns, from honu to volcanoes. Hawaiian Sudoku is by far the most creative Sudoku puzzle book out there. Happy puzzling.

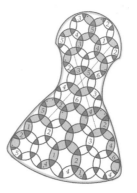

How to Play

As you noticed, this is not your ordinary Sudoku puzzle. It has been turned from squares into circles and hexagons. This puzzle plays with the same concept as regular Sudoku. The object is to fill in the empty spots.

The spaces around each and every circle/hexagon must contain the numbers 1 through 6, with <u>no repeated</u> numbers. The shaded spots that go in a straight line—vertically, horizontally, or diagonally—must also contain the numbers 1 through 6.

In the puzzle, some numbers have been filled in already. All you have to do is use pure logic to fill in the empty spots. Do not guess; it would spell disaster. If you guess wrong, the puzzle won't work out, and you'd have to start over.

There is no math involved; just some logical thinking and a little patience.

The spaces around each and every circle must contain the numbers 1 through 6, as shown here.

Connecting lines indicate a *shaded spot section,* in this case going diagonally.

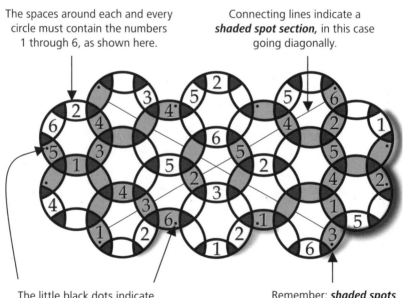

The little black dots indicate the beginning or ending of a *shaded spot section.*

Remember: *shaded spots* also have to contain the numbers 1 through 6.

6

Take a look at this puzzle. You see full circles, right? But take a closer look. All around the outer edges you see partial circles: 1/2 circles (with 3 numbers) and 1/3 circles (with 2 numbers), as shown by the dotted lines. Keep in mind that within these partial circles you cannot have the same numbers.

4, 3 and 5 are
in a 1/2 circle

6 and 4 are
in a 1/3 circle

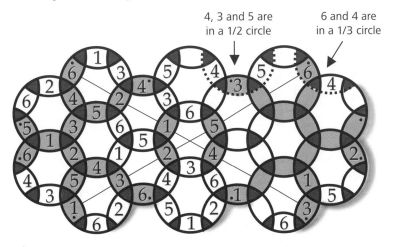

As mentioned earlier, the little dots indicate a 1 through 6 section. To give you a better idea of which dot goes to which dot, look at which corner the dot is in. If it's on the bottom ◆↑, then you would go across this spot and up. If it is here ◆↘, you would move diagonally to the other spot with a dot.

Tips:

When figuring out what number goes in a spot, look at its neighboring circles to see if they contain the same numbers. Say you're looking at circle D and trying to see where the number 4 goes. There are four open spots, but there are already 4s in circles A, C, and G. Therefore, the 4 has to go in the bottom middle spot of circle D.

Lets look at circle G. Can you figure out where the number 5 goes? It can't go in the top left because there's a 5 in circle D. The bottom left and bottom middle are part of shaded sections going diagonally. The diagonal section going from circle G to circle A already has a 5 in it (in circle A), so the 5 cannot go in either of the two empty spots. In the diagonal section going from circle E to circle K and continuing, there is already a 5 in circle I.

Besides, circle I is adjacent to circle G, and it already contains a 5 So the only place the 5 can go in is the top middle spot.

- When starting a puzzle, look for the circles with the most numbers.

- Look at the shaded spot sections, as these can be very helpful.

- When you fill in a number, look at its neighboring circles to see where you could put that same number.

Remember: do not guess. This is a logical puzzle. It will probably take you a few puzzles to get used to the new format, but you'll get the hang of it in no time. So get out your pencil and eraser (or a pen, but make sure you have white out), and get ready for a puzzling fun time.

There are three difficulty levels:

- Easy puzzles (1-40)

- Medium puzzles (41-80)

- Hard puzzles (81-120)

Solutions can be found on page 129.

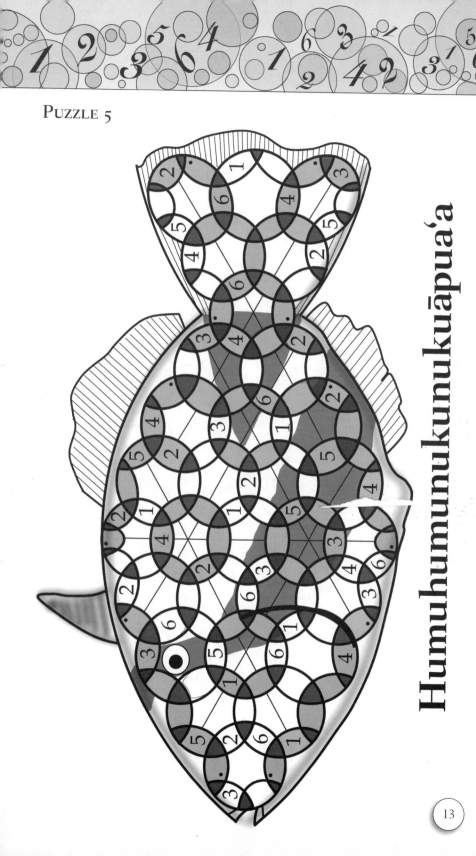

Humuhumunukunukuāpuaʻa

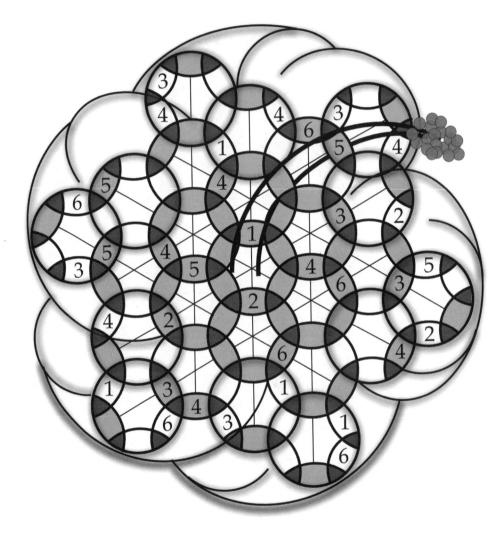

Hibiscus

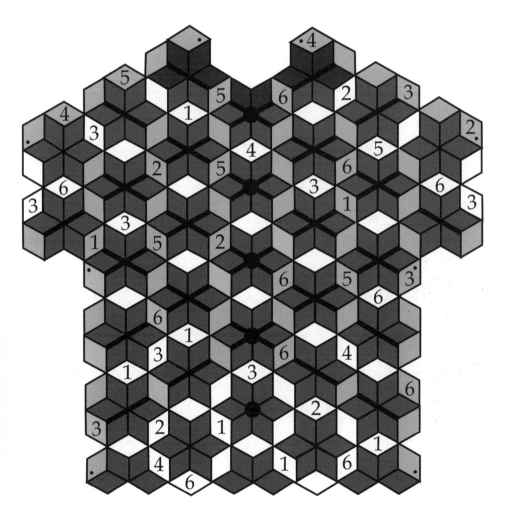

Aloha Shirt

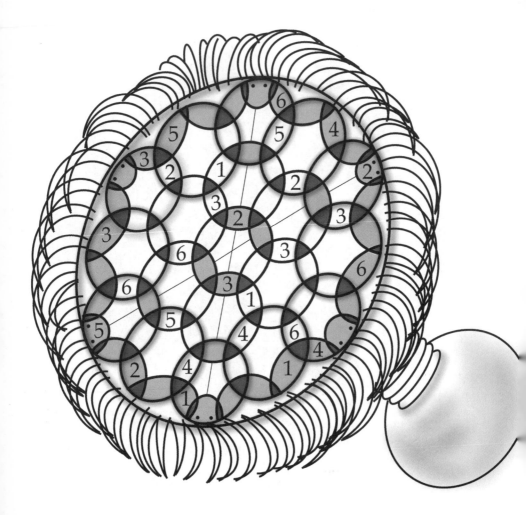

'Uli'uli

Surf's Up

Pineapple

PUZZLE 11

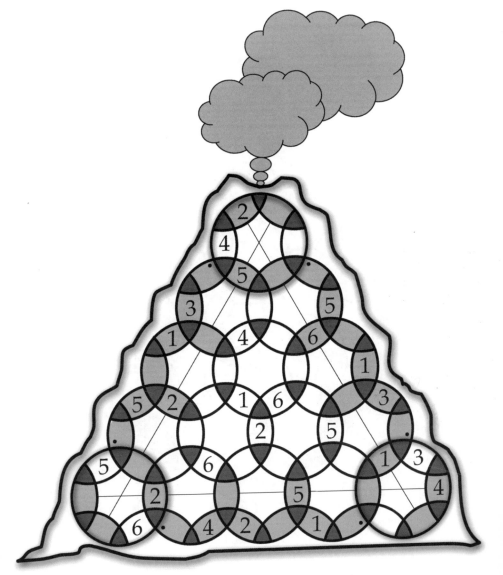

Volcano

Honu

PUZZLE 13

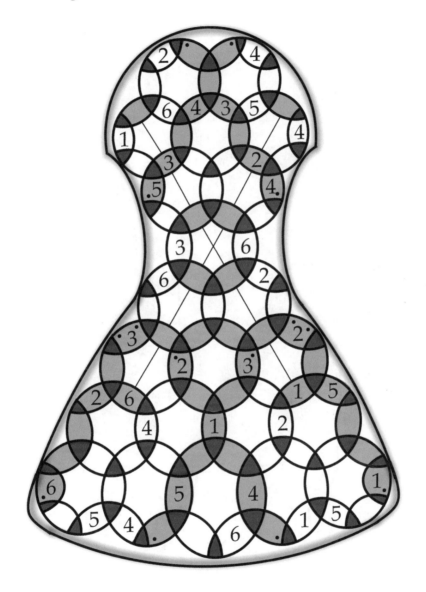

Poi Pounder

Pahu Drum

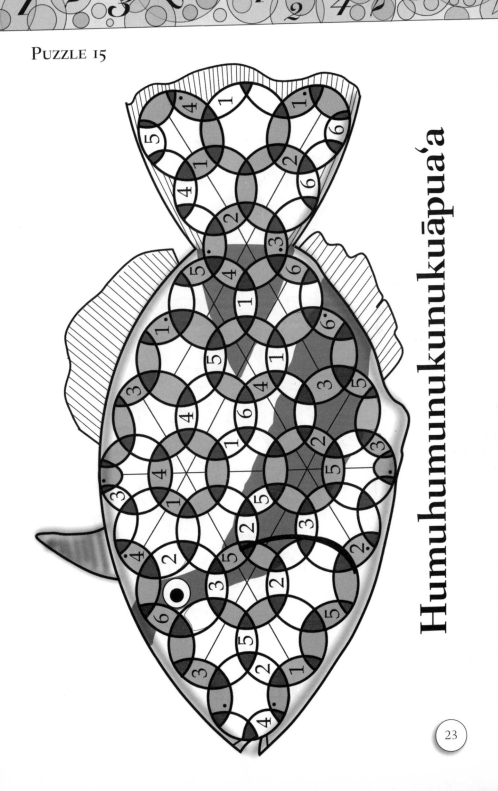

Humuhumunukunukuāpuaʻa

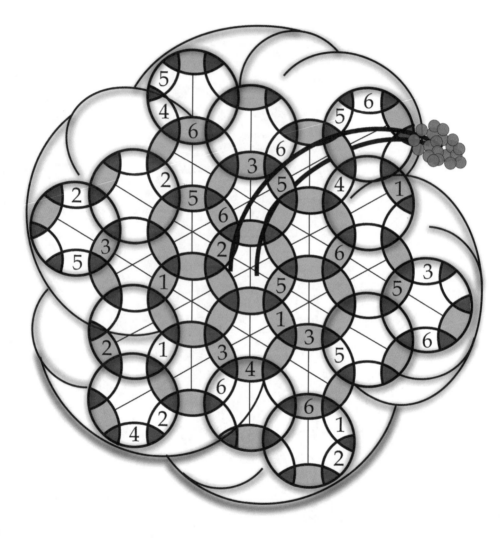

Hibiscus

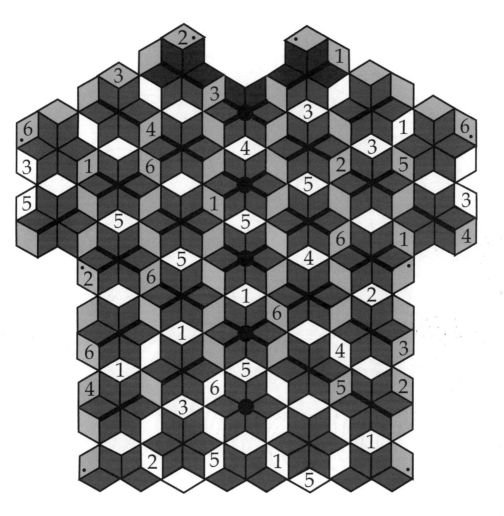

Aloha Shirt

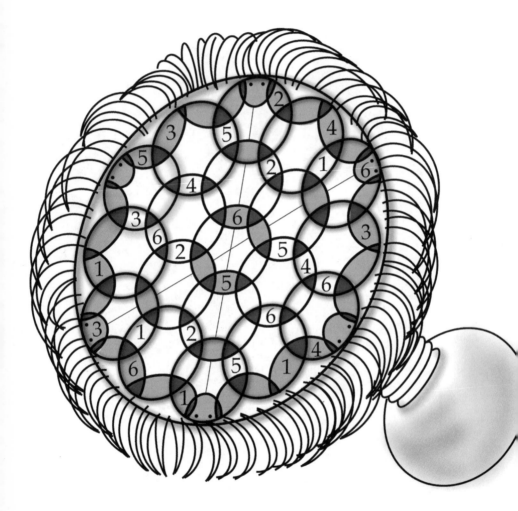

'Uli'uli

Surf's Up

Pineapple

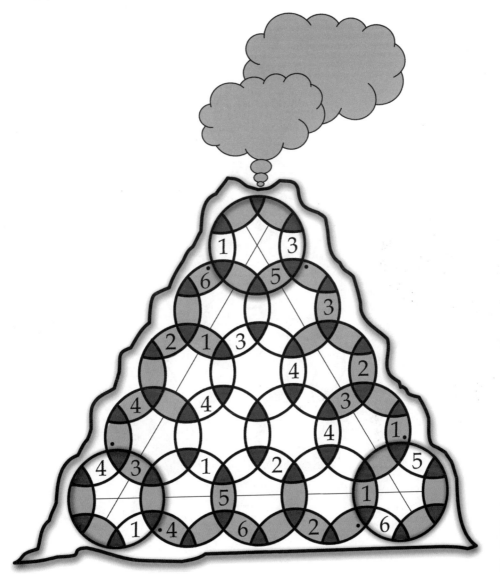

Volcano

Honu

PUZZLE 23

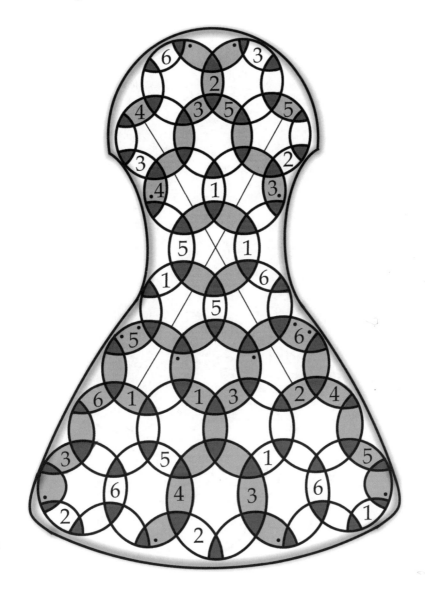

Poi Pounder

Pahu Drum

PUZZLE 25

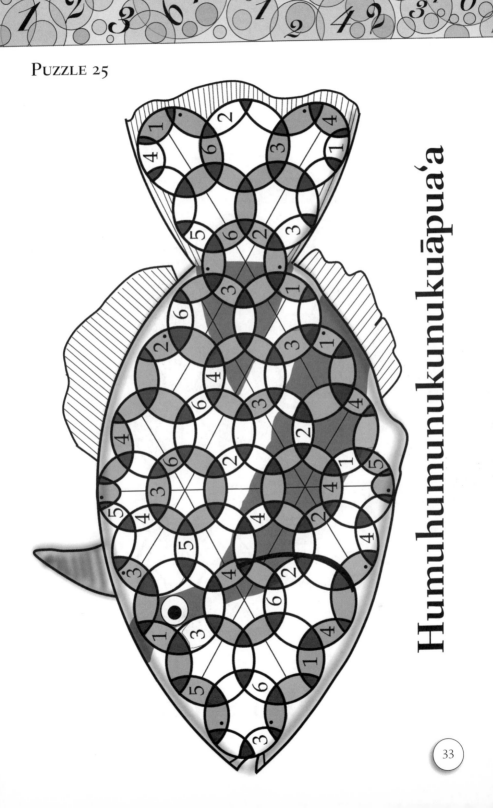

Humuhumunukunukuāpuaʻa

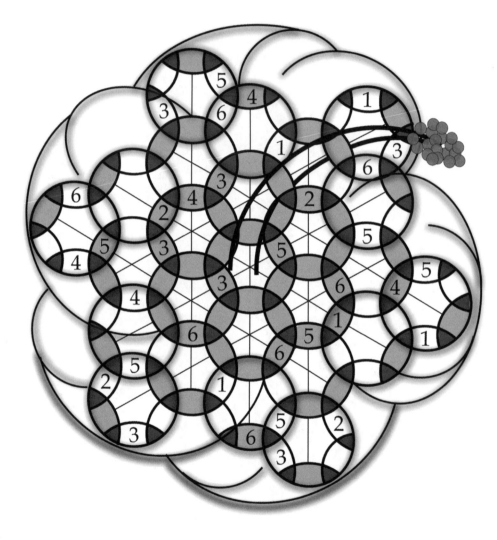

Hibiscus

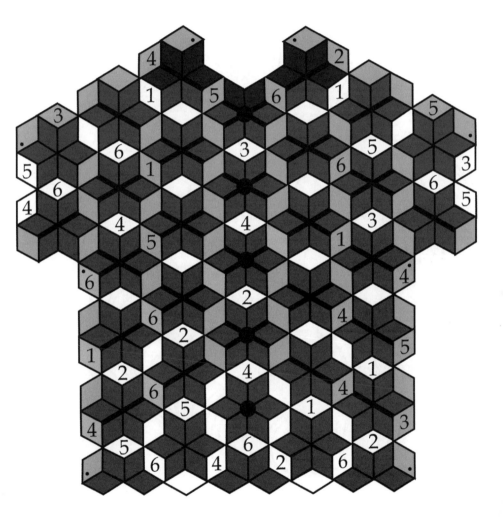

Aloha Shirt

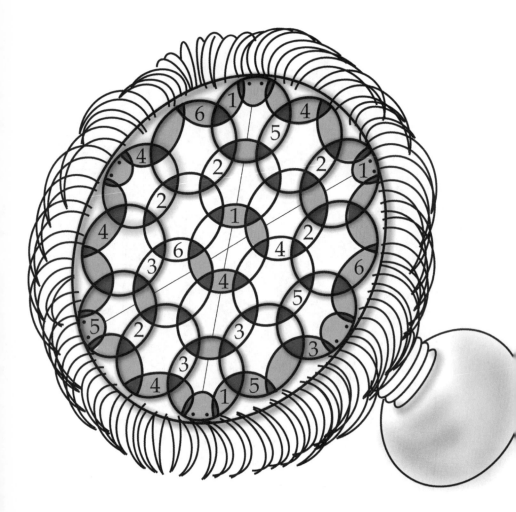

'Uli'uli

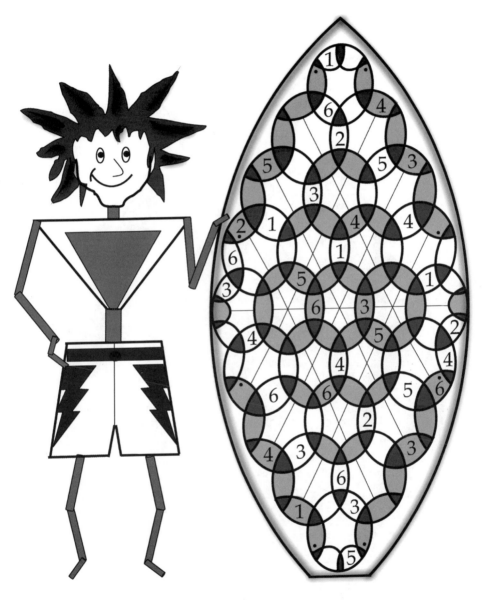

Surf's Up

Pineapple

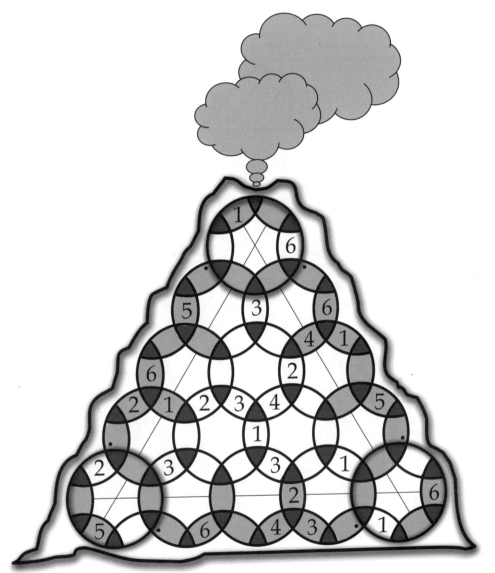

Volcano

Honu

PUZZLE 33

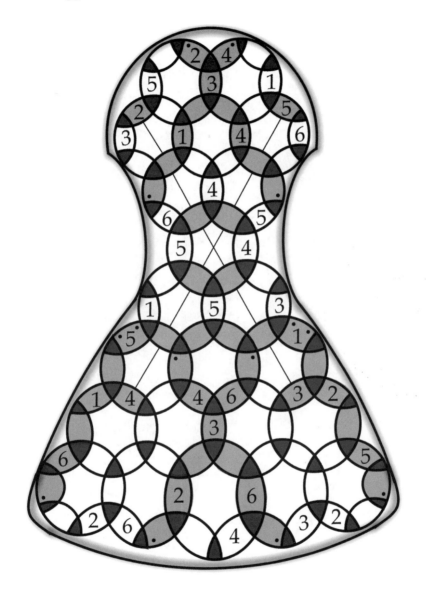

Poi Pounder

Pahu Drum

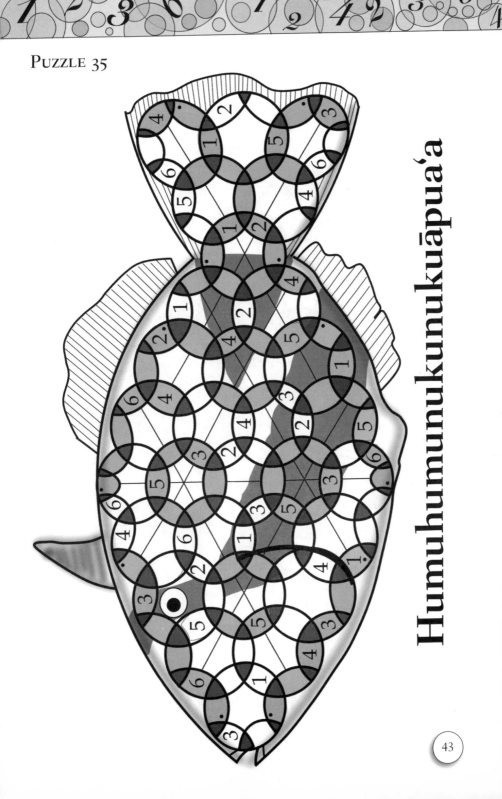

Humuhumunukunukuāpuaʻa

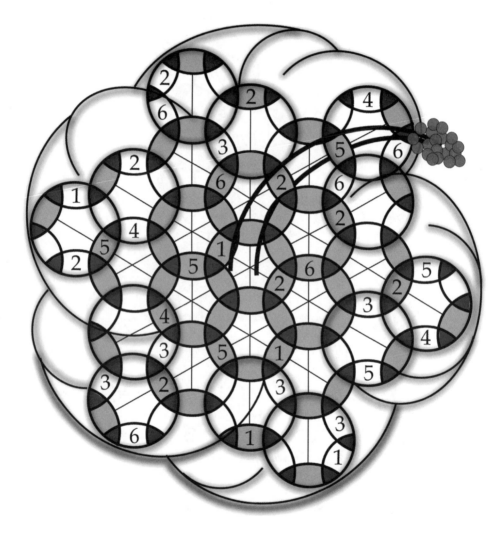

Hibiscus

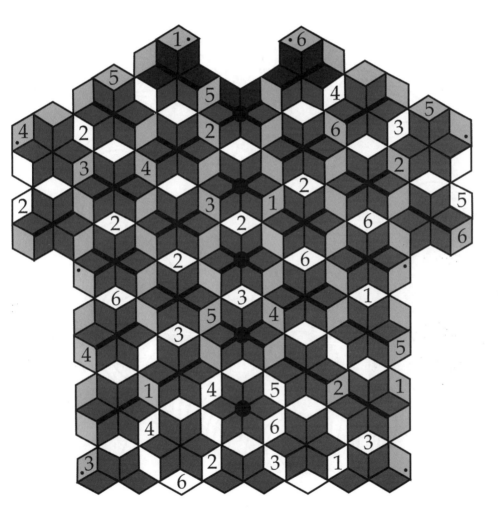

Aloha Shirt

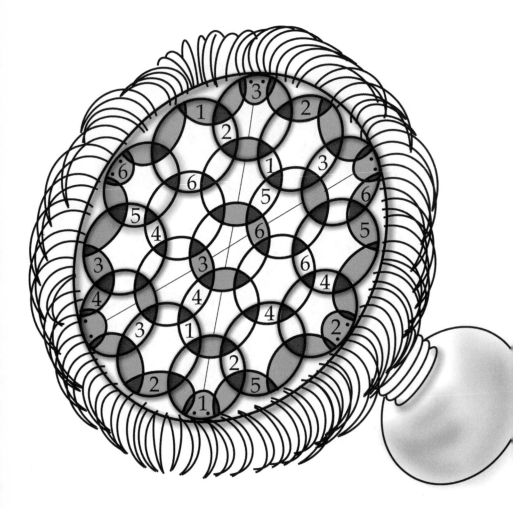

'Uli'uli

Surf's Up

Pineapple

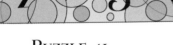

PUZZLE 41

Volcano

Honu

Puzzle 43

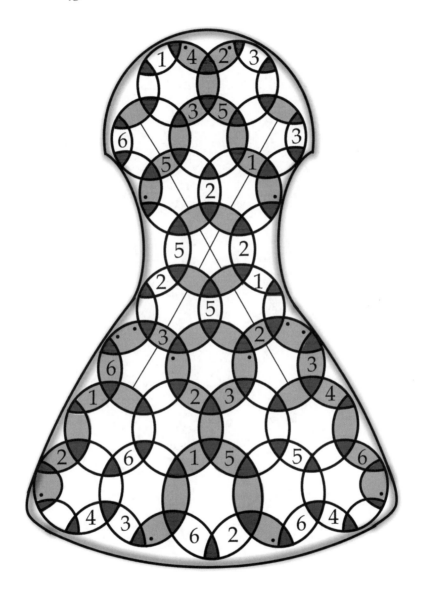

Poi Pounder

Pahu Drum

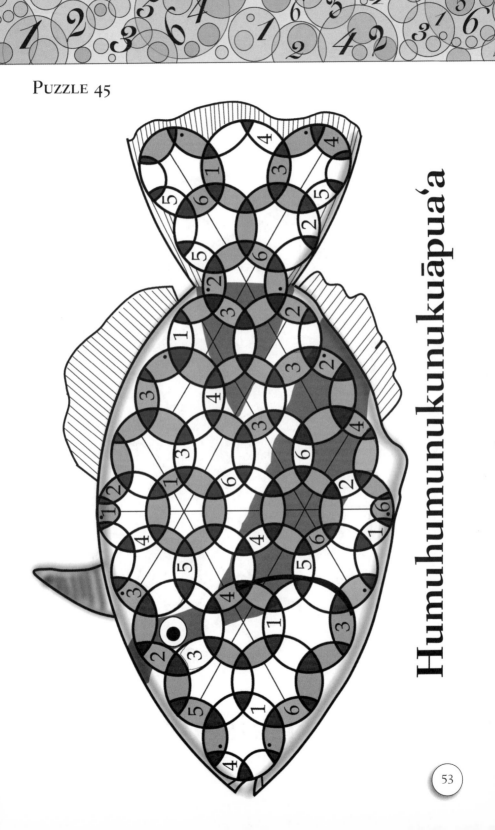

Humuhumunukunukuāpuaʻa

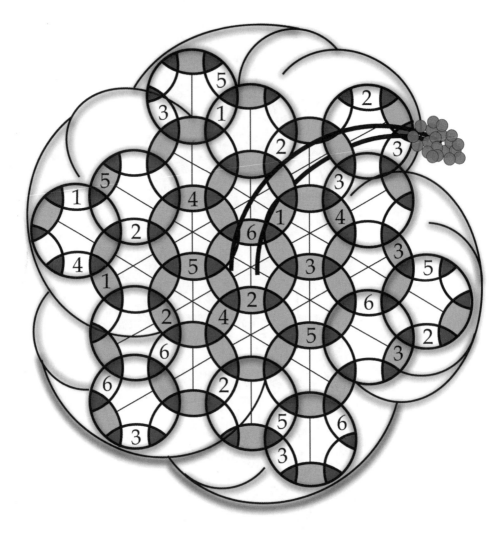

Hibiscus

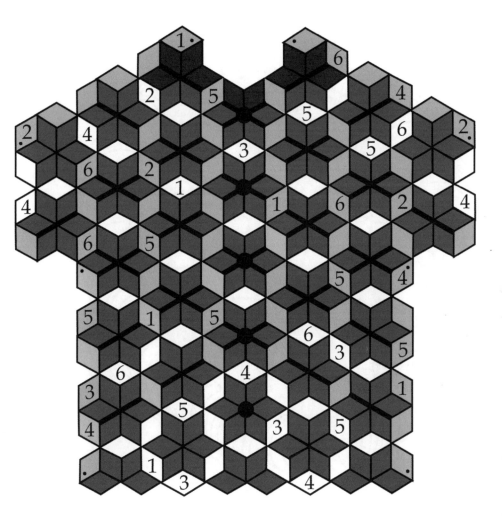

Aloha Shirt

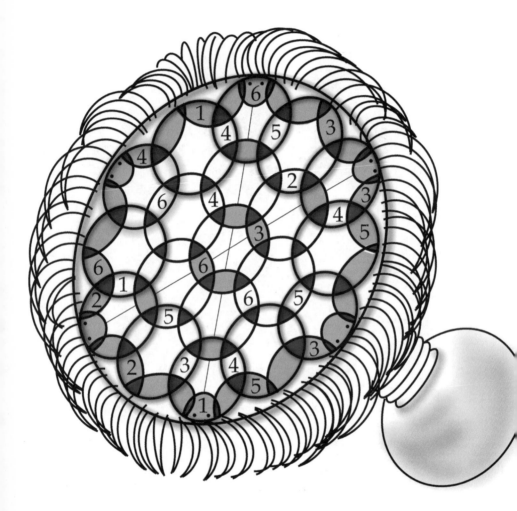

'Uli'uli

Surf's Up

Pineapple

PUZZLE 51

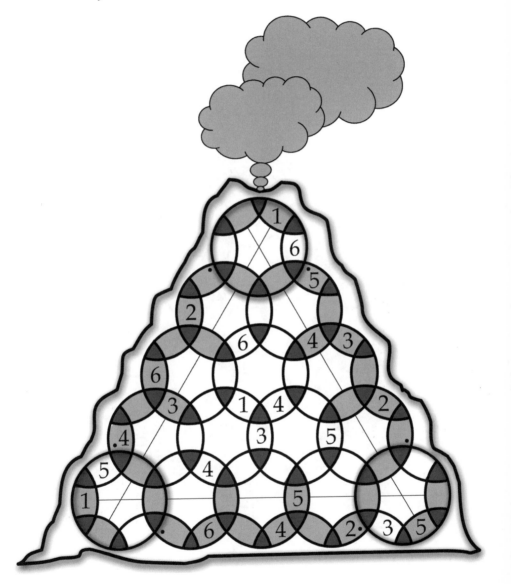

Volcano

Honu

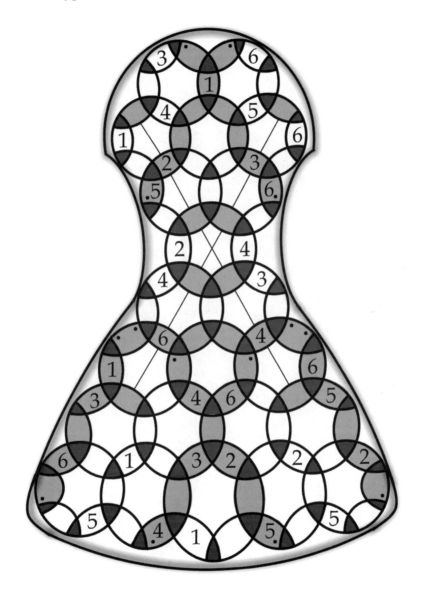

Poi Pounder

Pahu Drum

PUZZLE 55

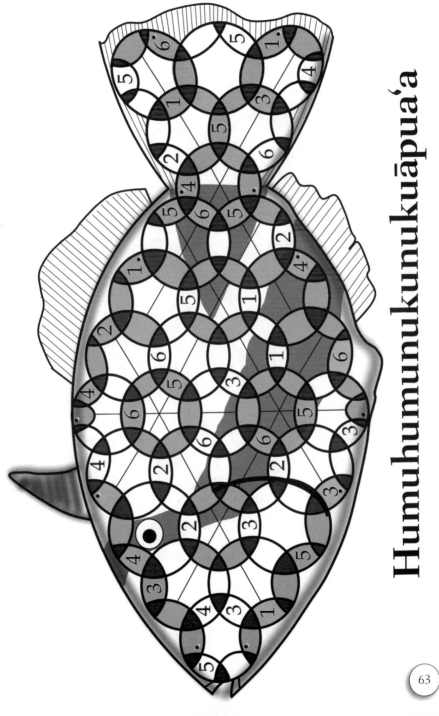

Humuhumunukunukuāpuaʻa

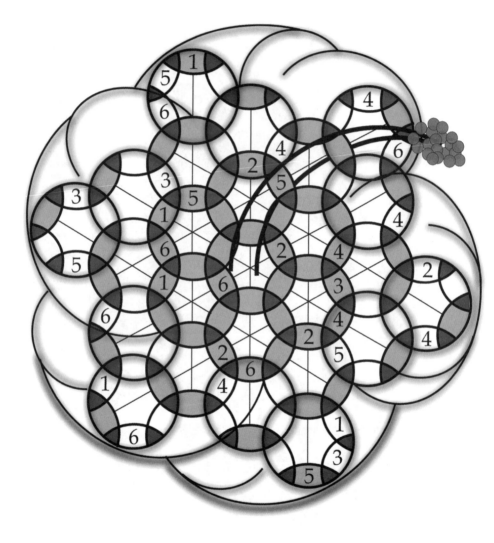

Hibiscus

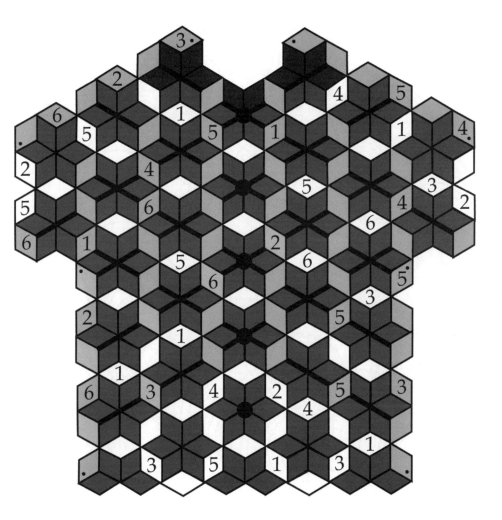

Aloha Shirt

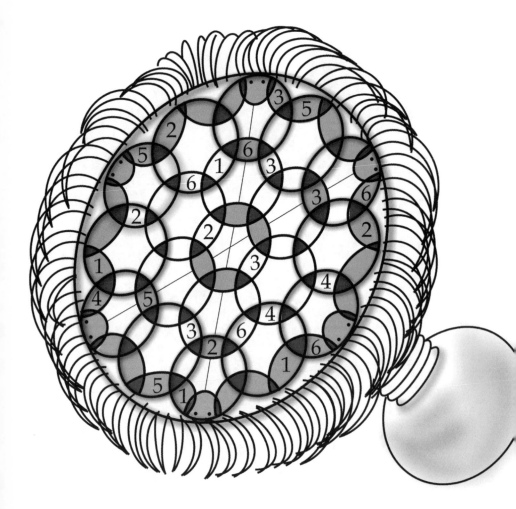

'Uli'uli

Surf's Up

Pineapple

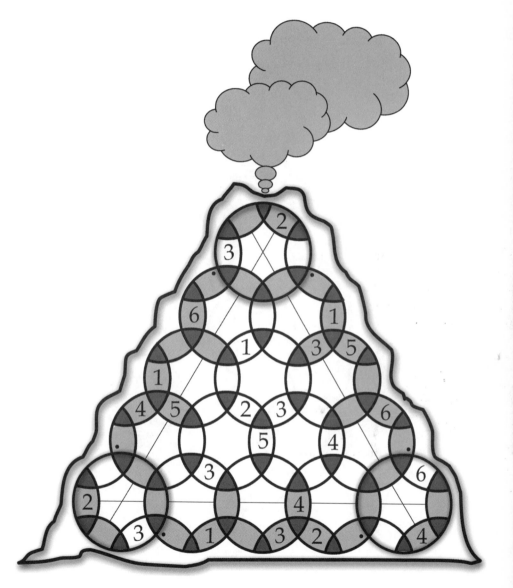

Volcano

Honu

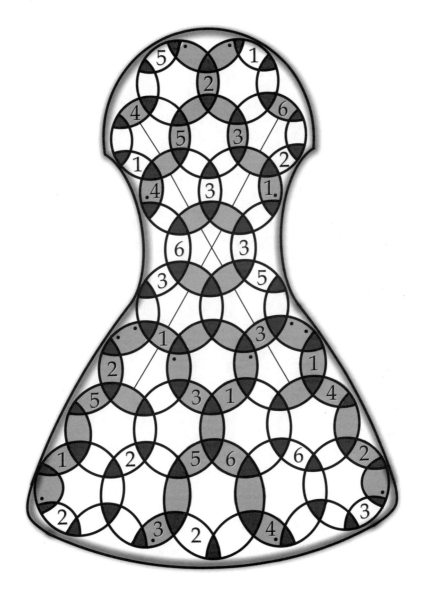

Poi Pounder

Pahu Drum

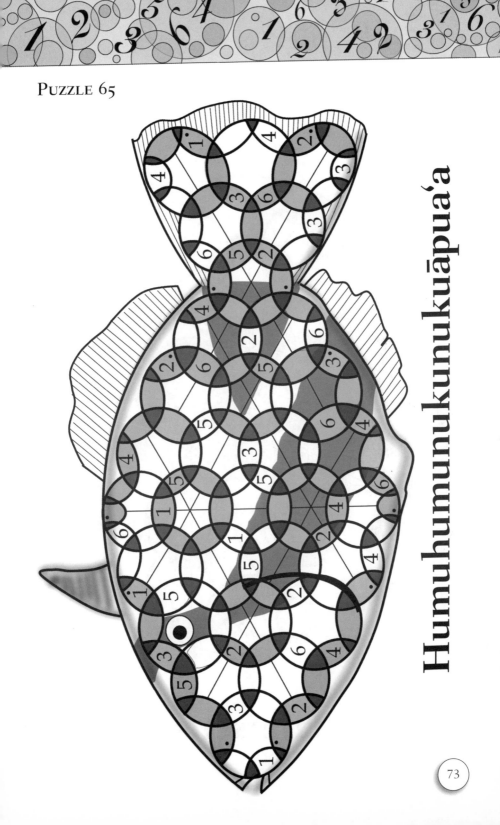

Humuhumunukunukuāpuaʻa

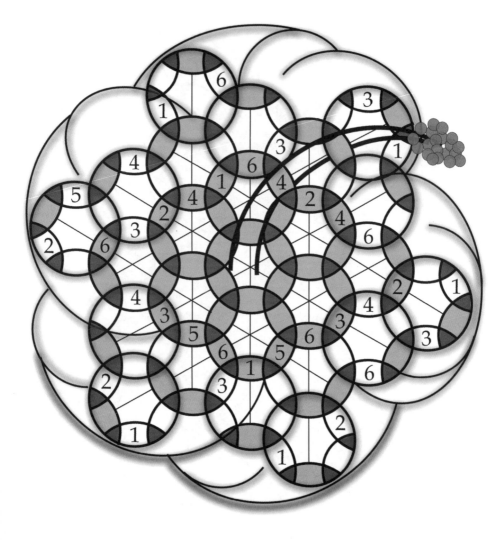

Hibiscus

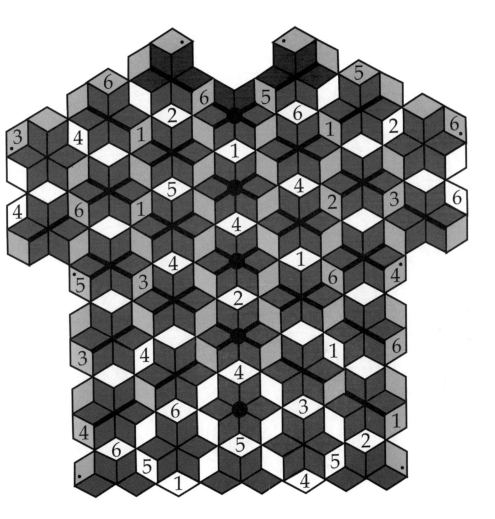

Aloha Shirt

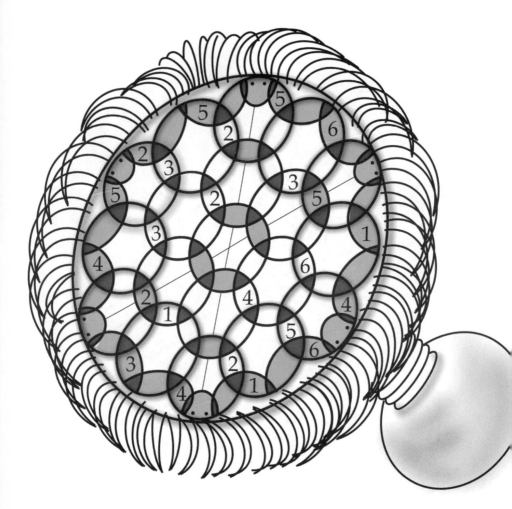

'Uli'uli

PUZZLE 69

Surf's Up

Pineapple

PUZZLE 71

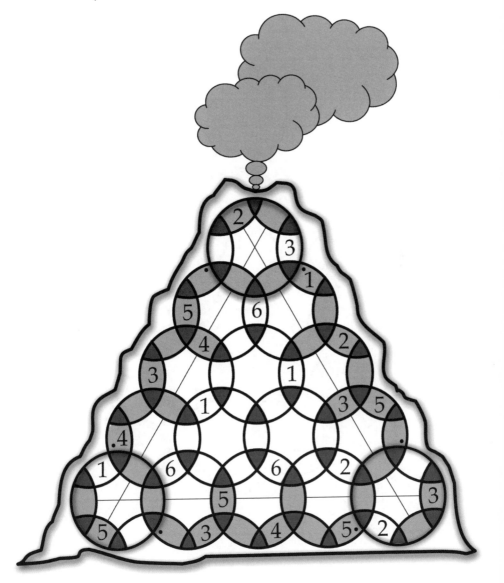

Volcano

Honu

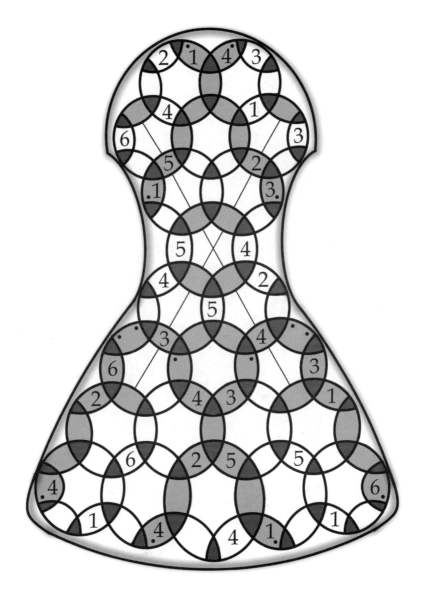

Poi Pounder

Pahu Drum

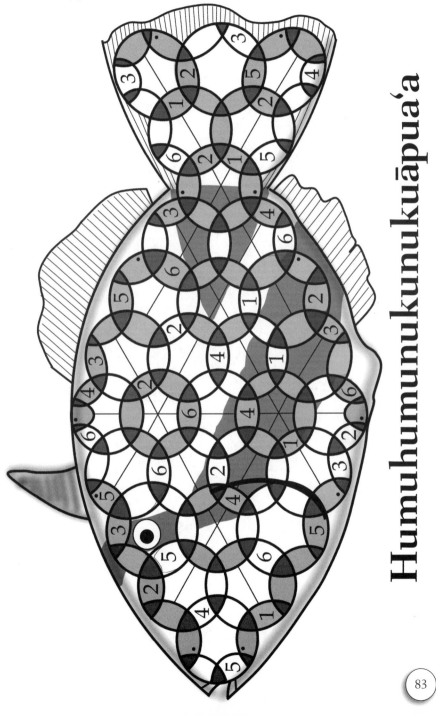

Humuhumunukunukuāpuaʻa

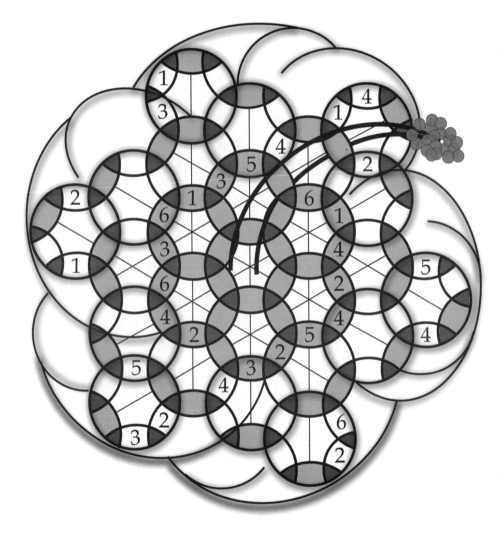

Hibiscus

PUZZLE 77

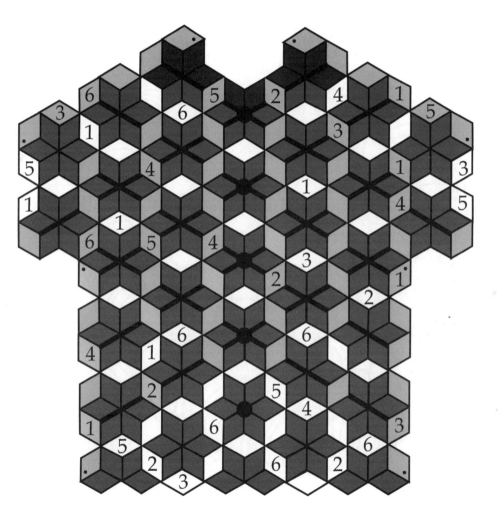

Aloha Shirt

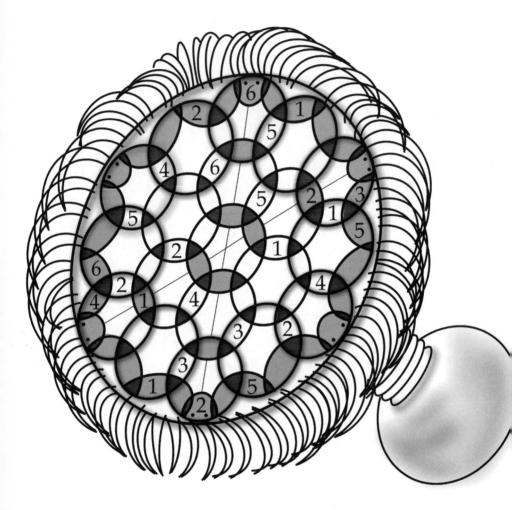

'Uli'uli

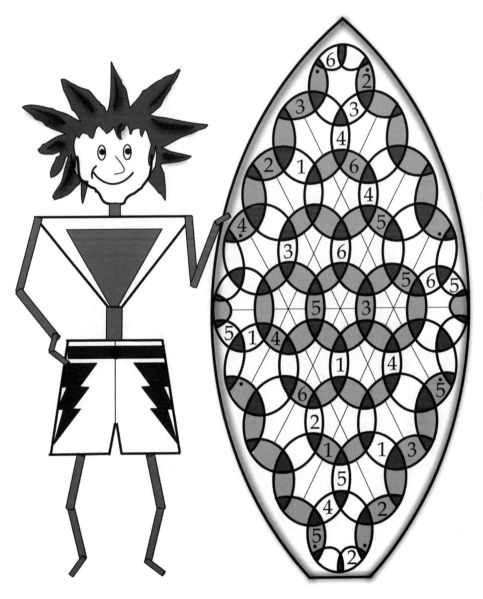

Surf's Up

Pineapple

PUZZLE 81

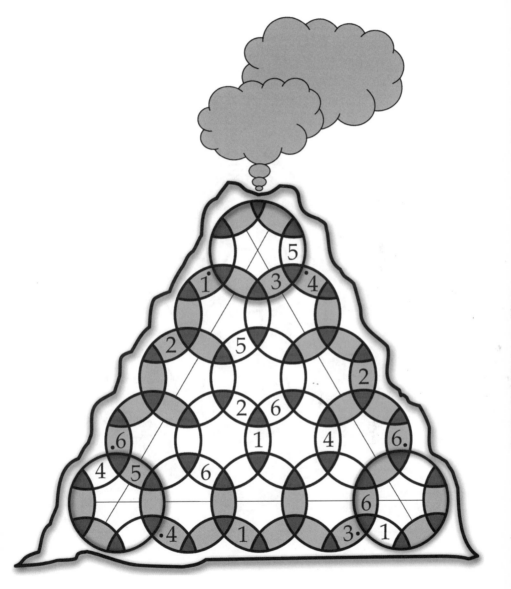

Volcano

Honu

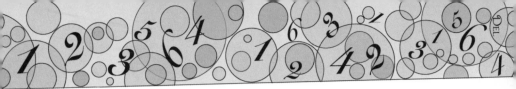

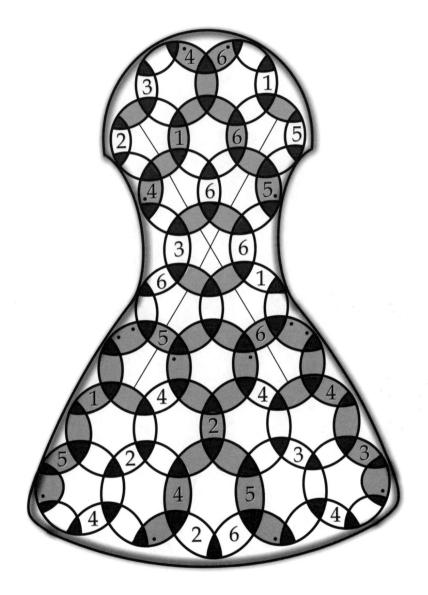

Poi Pounder

Pahu Drum

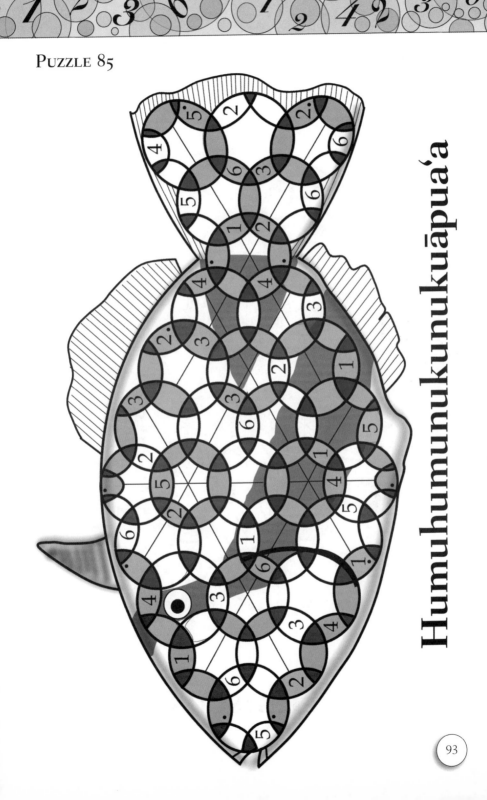

Humuhumunukunukuāpuaʻa

PUZZLE 86

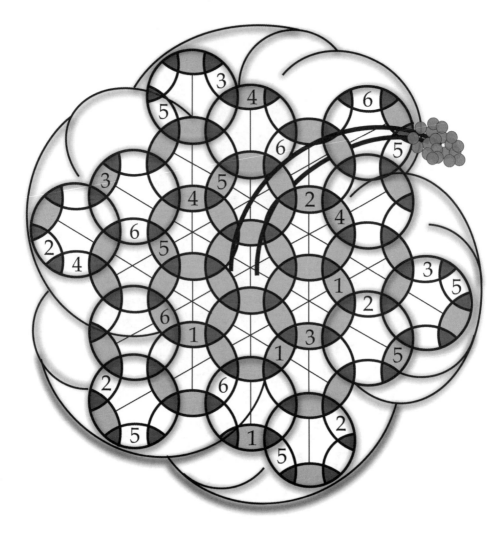

Hibiscus

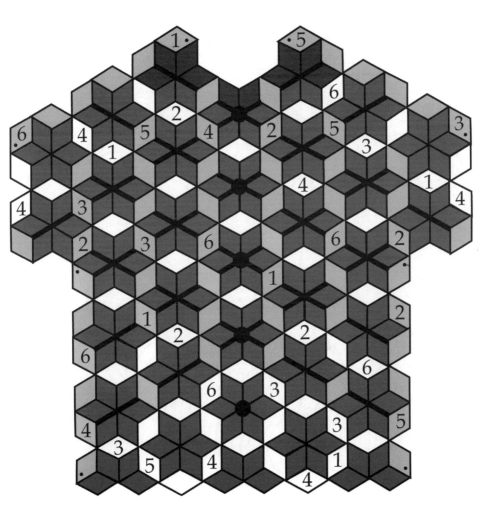

Aloha Shirt

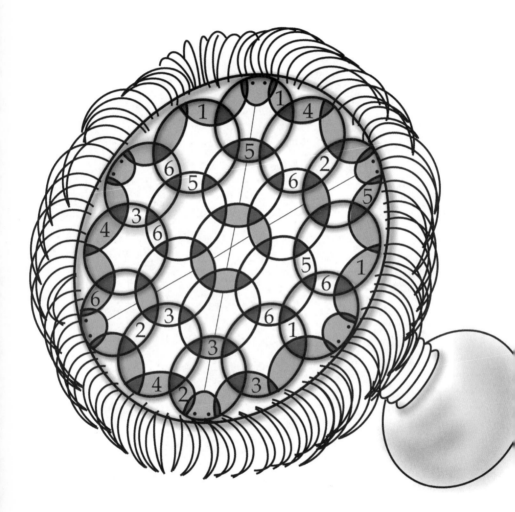

'Uli'uli

Puzzle 89

Surf's Up

Pineapple

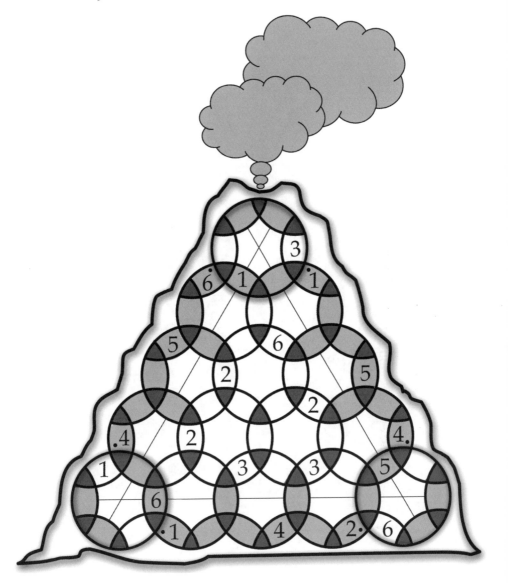

Volcano

Honu

PUZZLE 93

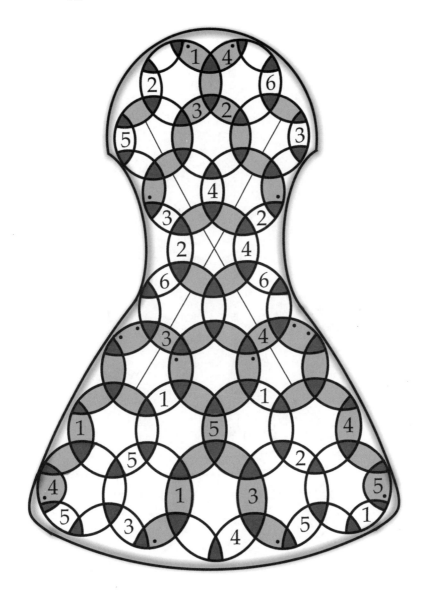

Poi Pounder

Pahu Drum

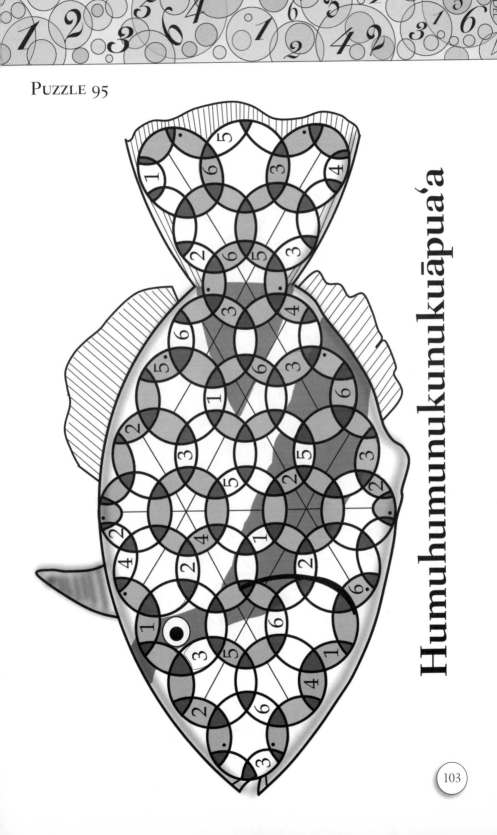

Humuhumunukunukuāpuaʻa

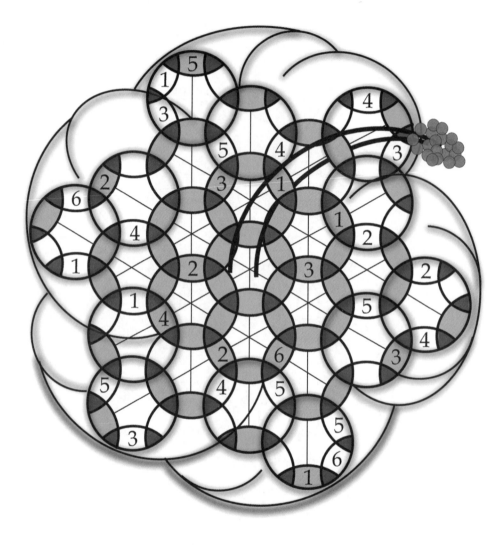

Hibiscus

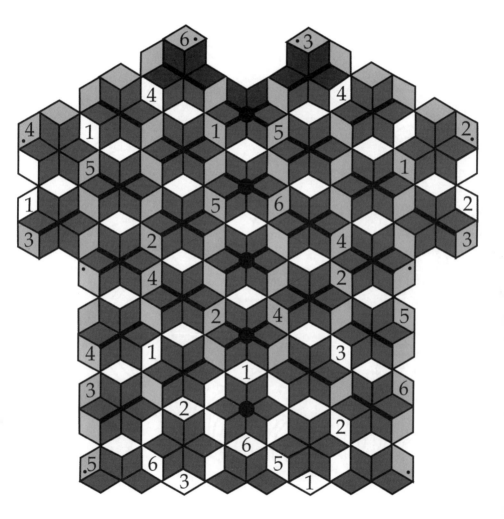

Aloha Shirt

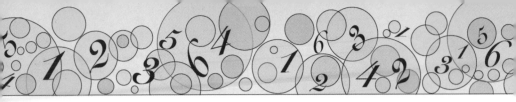

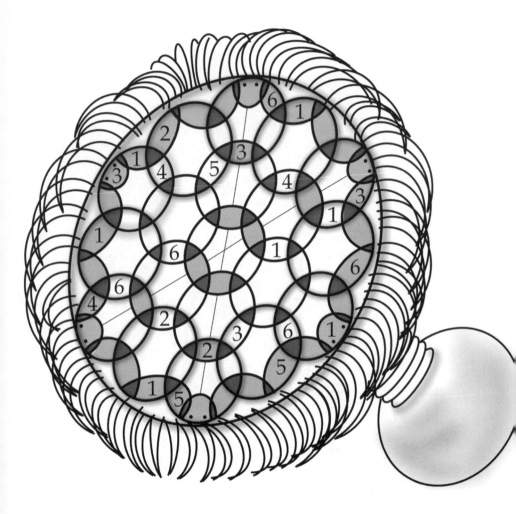

'Uli'uli

Surf's Up

Pineapple

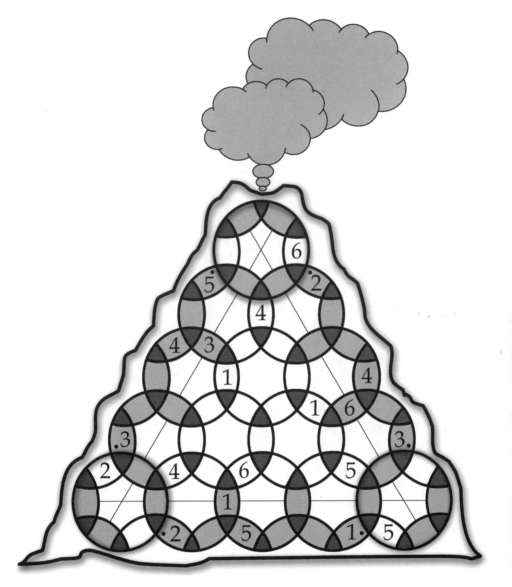

Volcano

Honu

PUZZLE 103

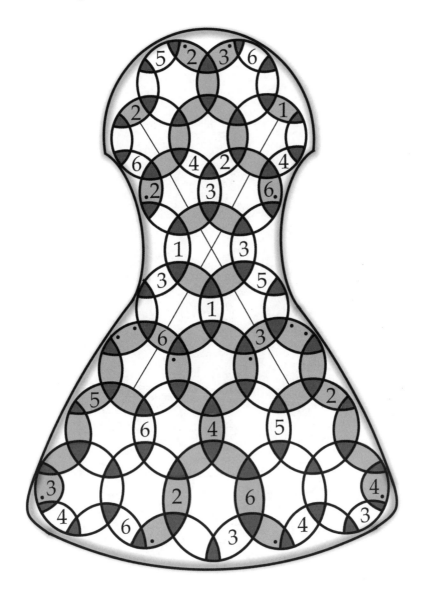

Poi Pounder

PUZZLE 104

Pahu Drum

Puzzle 105

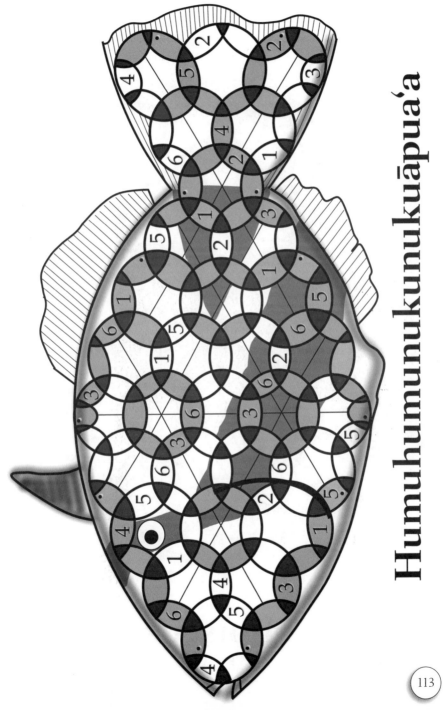

Humuhumunukunukuāpuaʻa

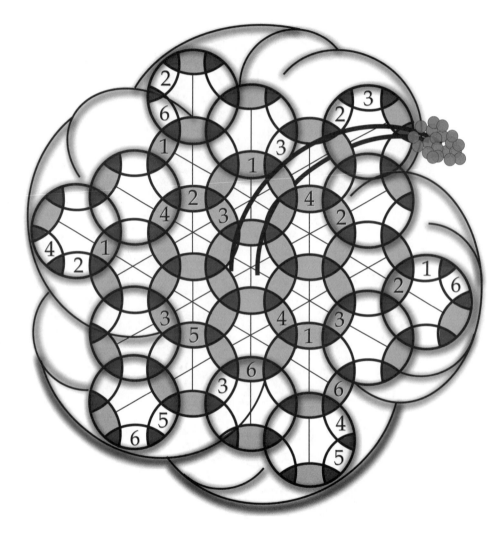

Hibiscus

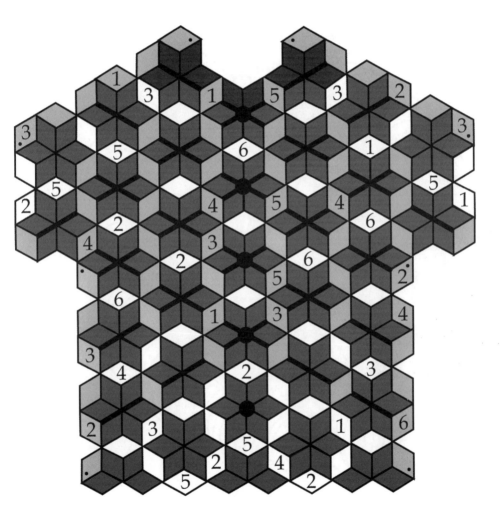

Aloha Shirt

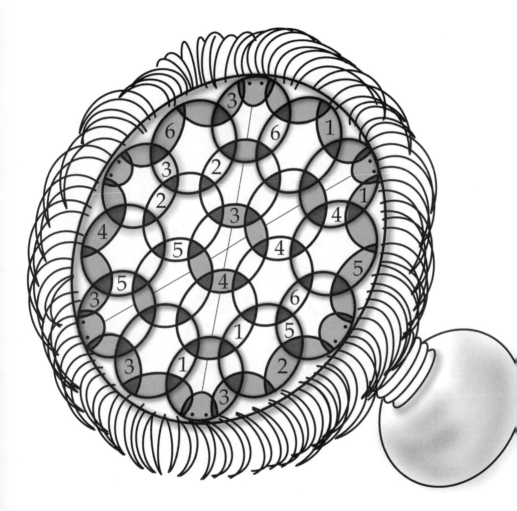

'Uli'uli

PUZZLE 109

Surf's Up

Pineapple

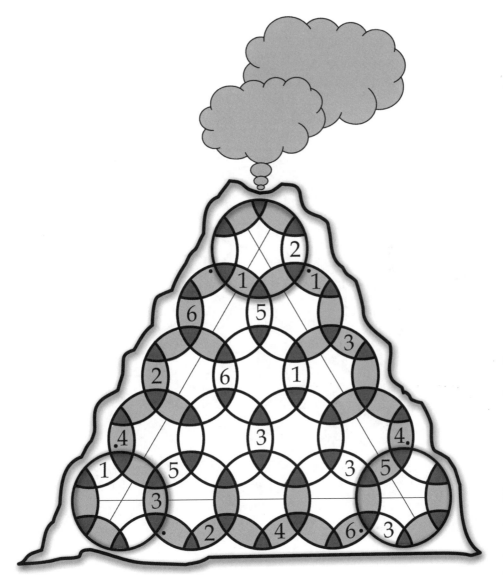

Volcano

Honu

PUZZLE 113

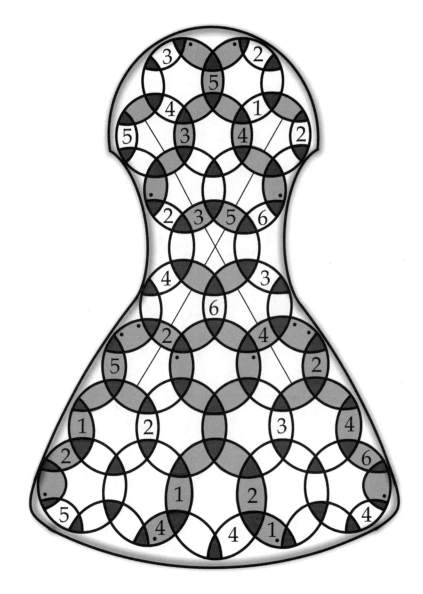

Poi Pounder

Pahu Drum

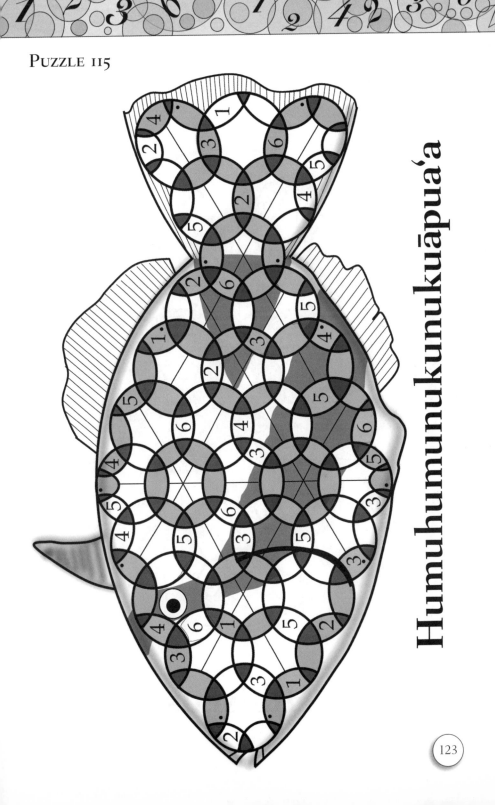

Humuhumunukunukuāpuaʻa

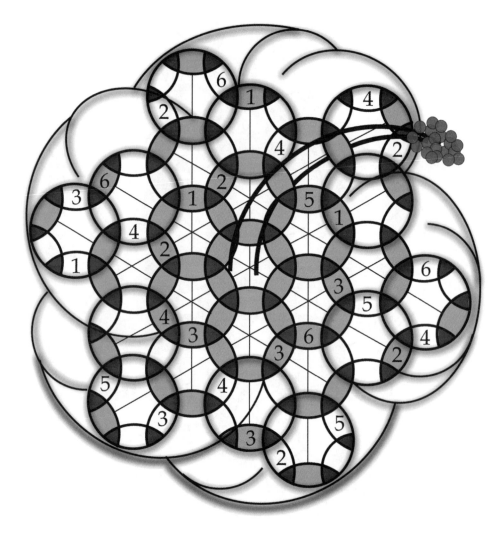

Hibiscus

Puzzle 117

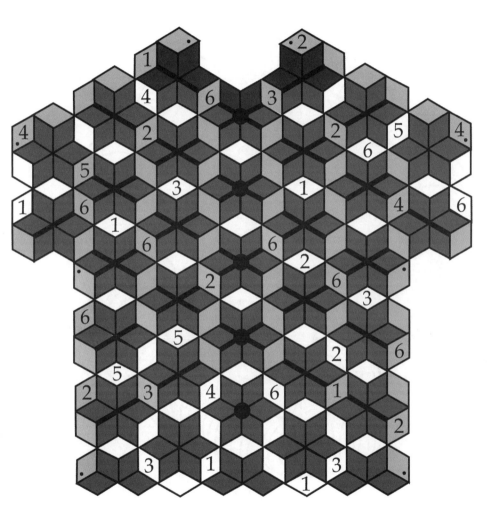

Aloha Shirt

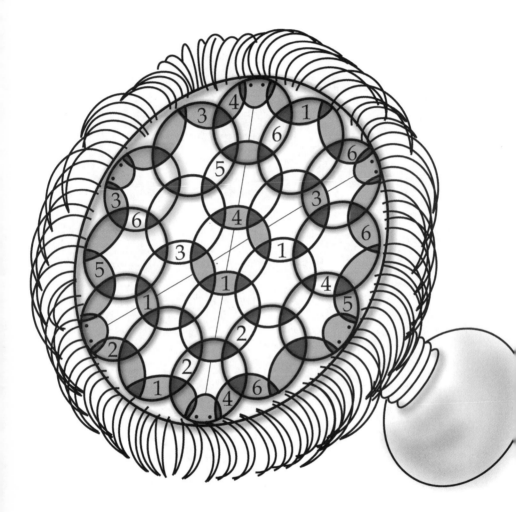

'Uli'uli

Surf's Up

Pineapple

Solutions

Here you go, I'll give you the answers.

Solutions

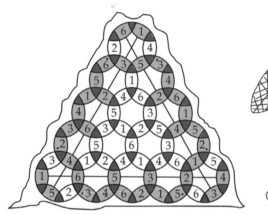

PUZZLE 1

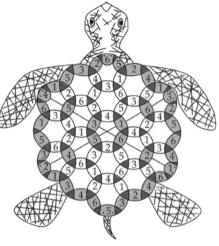

PUZZLE 2

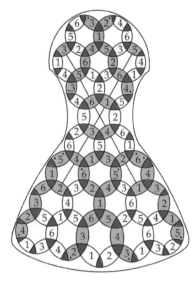

PUZZLE 3

PUZZLE 4

Solutions

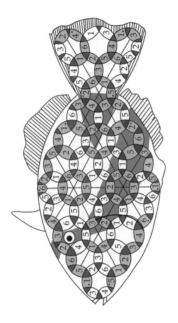

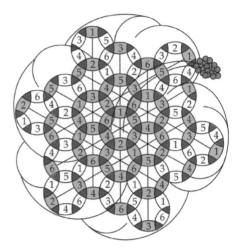

PUZZLE 5

PUZZLE 6

PUZZLE 7

PUZZLE 8

Solutions

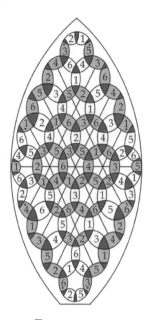

PUZZLE 9

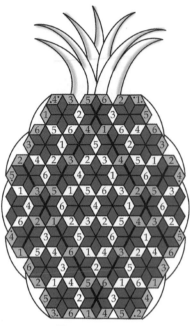

PUZZLE 10

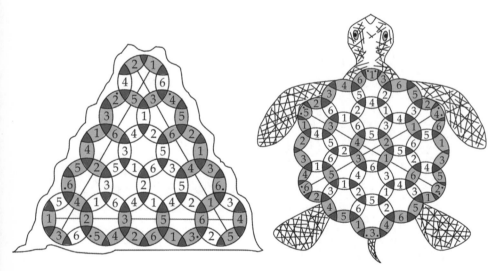

PUZZLE 11

PUZZLE 12

Solutions

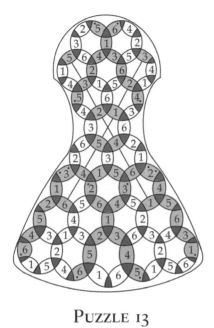

PUZZLE 13

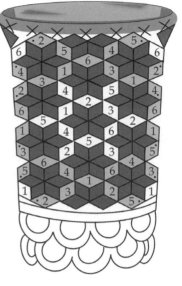

PUZZLE 14

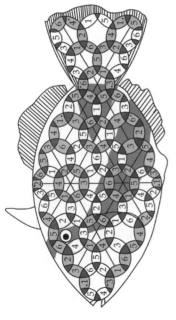

PUZZLE 15

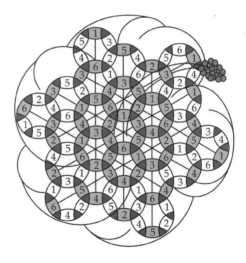

PUZZLE 16

Solutions

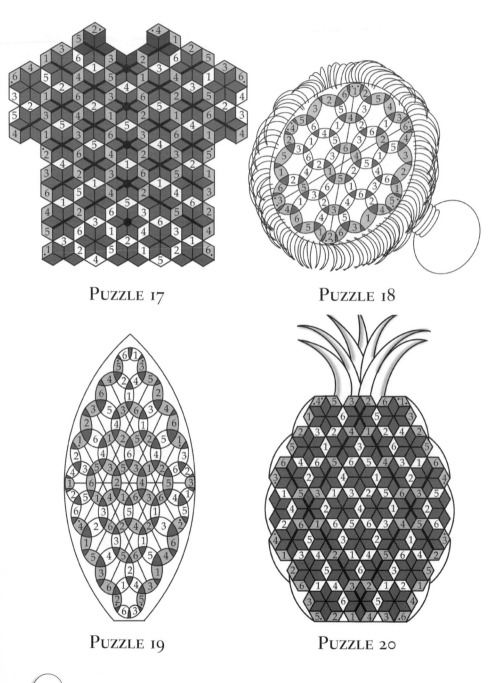

Puzzle 17

Puzzle 18

Puzzle 19

Puzzle 20

Solutions

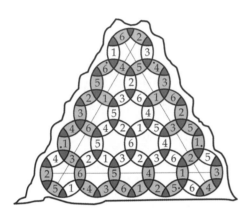

Puzzle 21

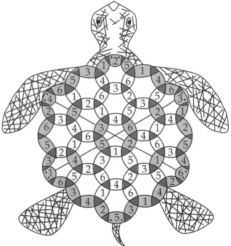

Puzzle 22

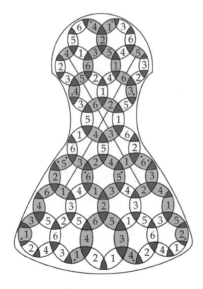

Puzzle 23

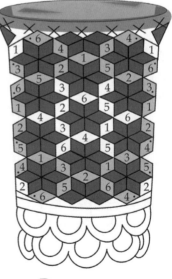

Puzzle 24

Solutions

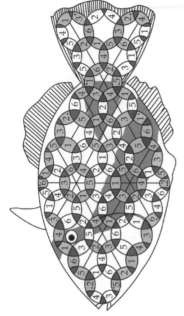

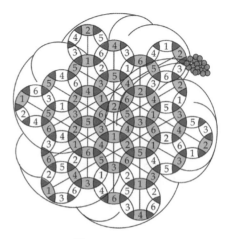

PUZZLE 25

PUZZLE 26

PUZZLE 27

PUZZLE 28

Solutions

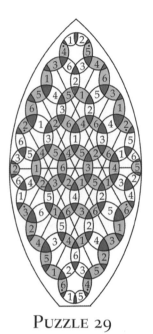

PUZZLE 29

PUZZLE 30

PUZZLE 31

PUZZLE 32

Solutions

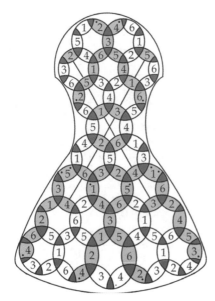

PUZZLE 33

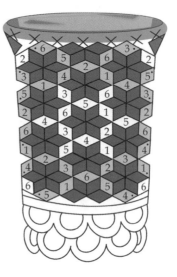

PUZZLE 34

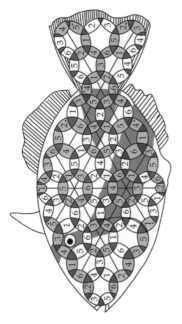

PUZZLE 35

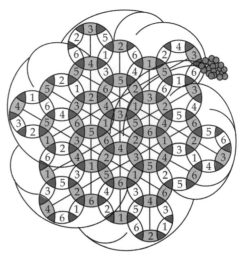

PUZZLE 36

Solutions

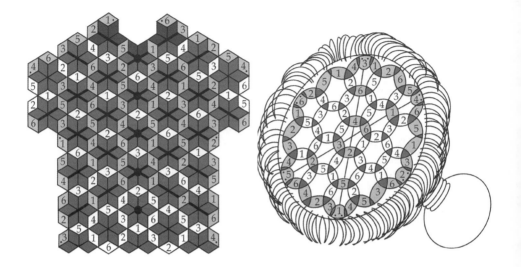

PUZZLE 37

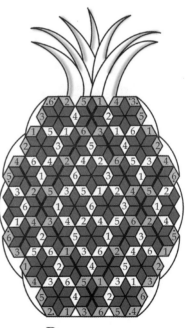

PUZZLE 38

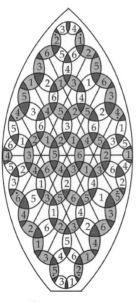

PUZZLE 39

PUZZLE 40

Solutions

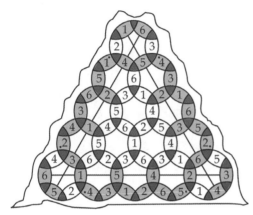

PUZZLE 41

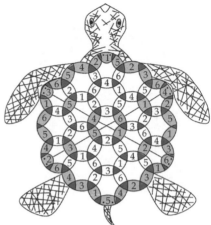

PUZZLE 42

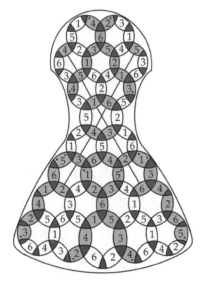

PUZZLE 43

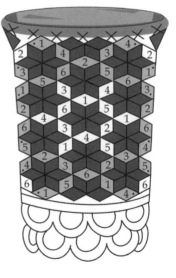

PUZZLE 44

Solutions

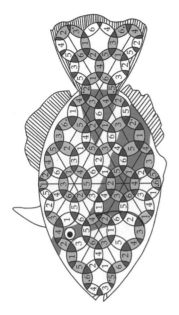

PUZZLE 45

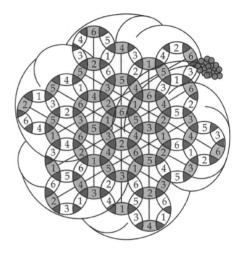

PUZZLE 46

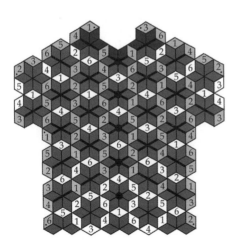

PUZZLE 47

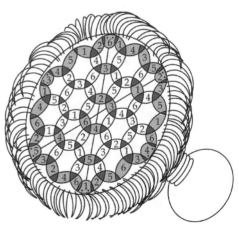

PUZZLE 48

Solutions

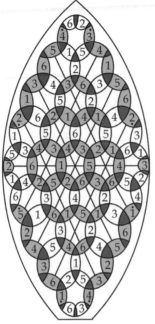

Puzzle 49

Puzzle 50

Puzzle 51

Puzzle 52

Solutions

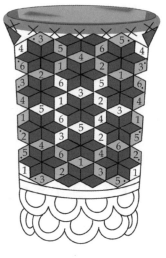

PUZZLE 53

PUZZLE 54

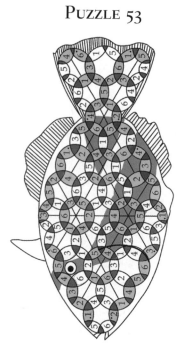

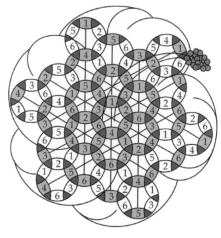

PUZZLE 55

PUZZLE 56

Solutions

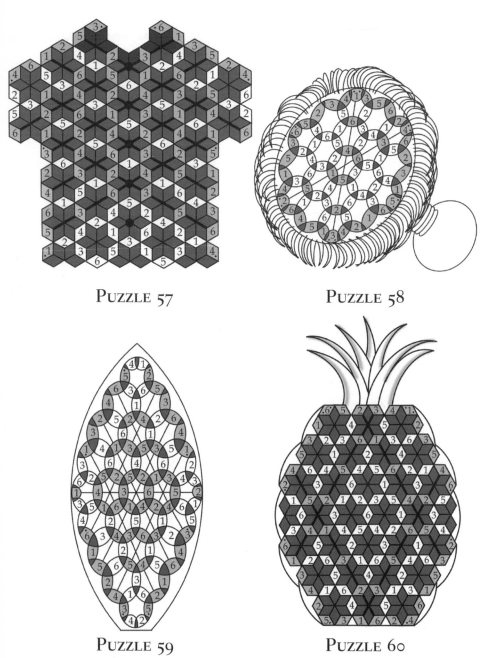

PUZZLE 57

PUZZLE 58

PUZZLE 59

PUZZLE 60

Solutions

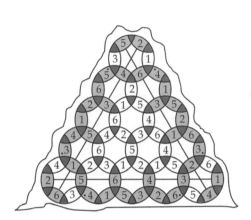

PUZZLE 61

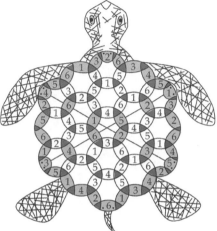

PUZZLE 62

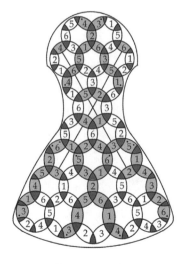

PUZZLE 63

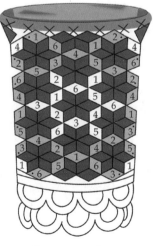

PUZZLE 64

145

Solutions

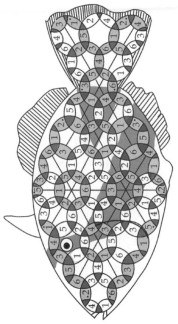

PUZZLE 65

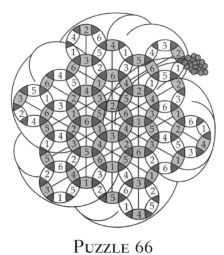

PUZZLE 66

PUZZLE 67

PUZZLE 68

Solutions

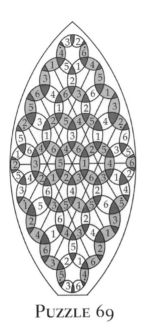

PUZZLE 69

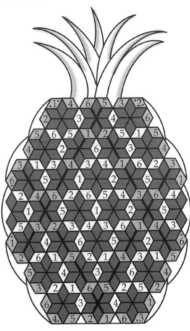

PUZZLE 70

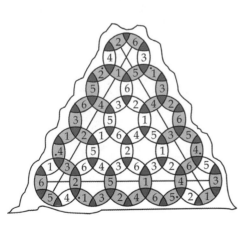

PUZZLE 71

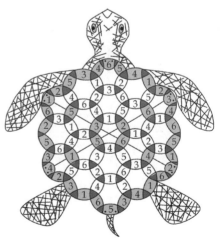

PUZZLE 72

Solutions

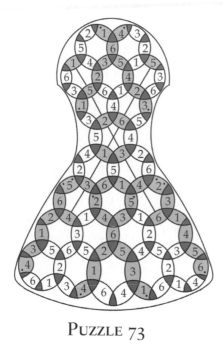

PUZZLE 73

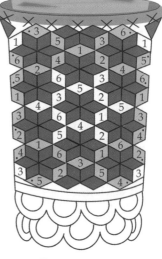

PUZZLE 74

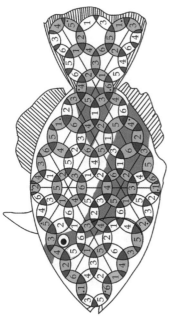

PUZZLE 75

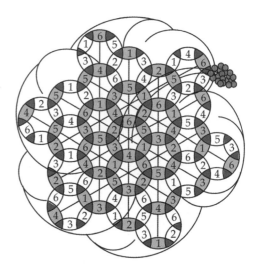

PUZZLE 76

Solutions

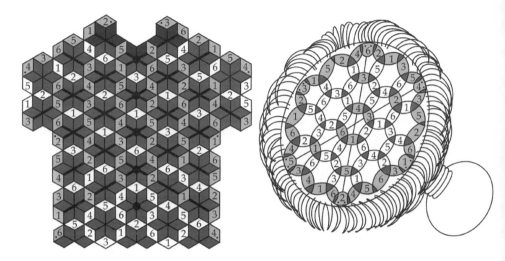

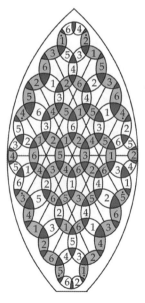

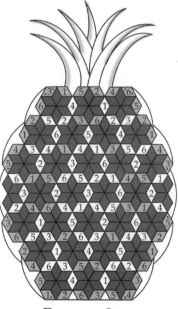

PUZZLE 77

PUZZLE 78

PUZZLE 79

PUZZLE 80

Solutions

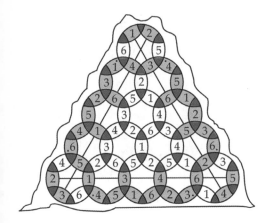

PUZZLE 81

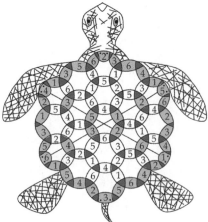

PUZZLE 82

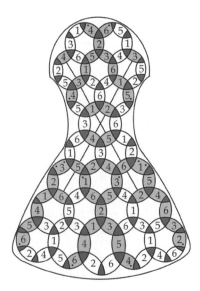

PUZZLE 83

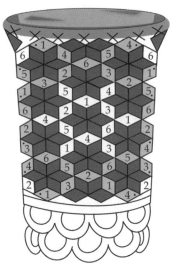

PUZZLE 84

Solutions

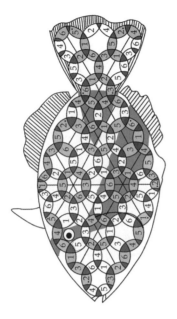

PUZZLE 85

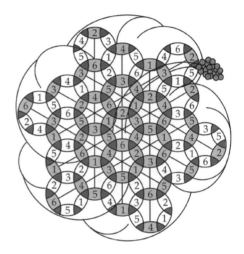

PUZZLE 86

PUZZLE 87

PUZZLE 88

Solutions

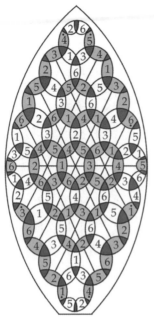

PUZZLE 89

PUZZLE 90

PUZZLE 91

PUZZLE 92

Solutions

PUZZLE 93

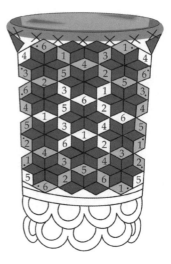

PUZZLE 94

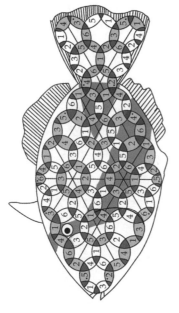

PUZZLE 95

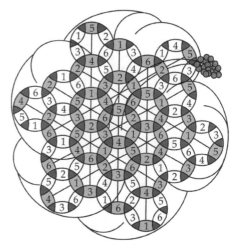

PUZZLE 96

Solutions

PUZZLE 97

PUZZLE 98

PUZZLE 99

PUZZLE 100

Solutions

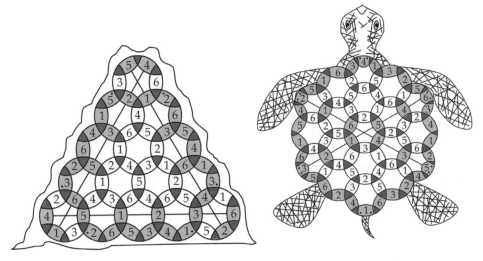

PUZZLE 101

PUZZLE 102

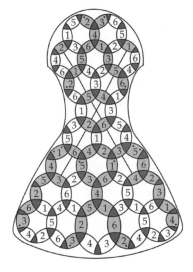

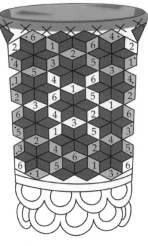

PUZZLE 103

PUZZLE 104

Solutions

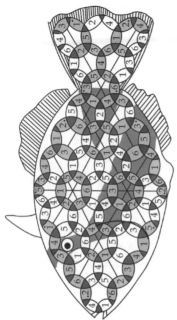

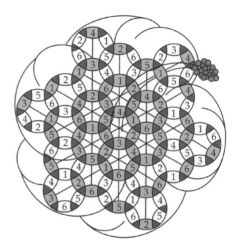

PUZZLE 105

PUZZLE 106

PUZZLE 107

PUZZLE 108

Solutions

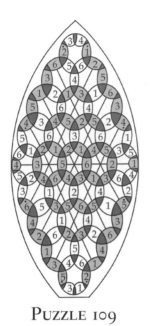

PUZZLE 109

PUZZLE 110

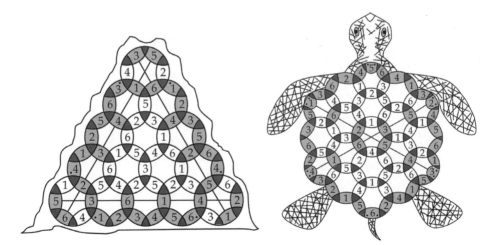

PUZZLE 111

PUZZLE 112

Solutions

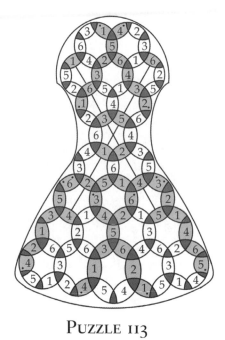

PUZZLE 113

PUZZLE 114

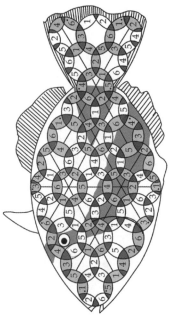

PUZZLE 115

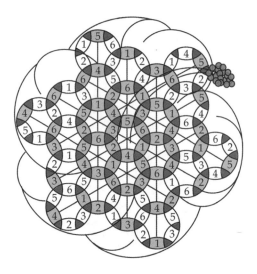

PUZZLE 116

Solutions

PUZZLE 117

PUZZLE 118

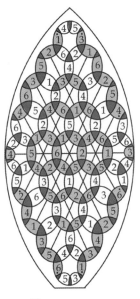

PUZZLE 119

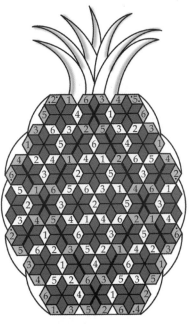

PUZZLE 120

About the Author

Delwyn Higa, the creator of Hawaiian Sudoku, was born, raised, and still lives in Hawaiʻi. He takes great pride in creating these puzzles, especially since he is from Hawaiʻi and loves the Islands very much. Delwyn has been an entrepreneur for over 25 years. He owns and operates a retail jewelry store/manufactory shop that specializes in Hawaiian Heirloom Jewelry. He is a jewelry designer and a custom hand engraver, and he is regarded as one of the top Master Engravers in Hawaiʻi.